FIRST PAST THE POST®

Verbal Reasoning:
CLOZE TESTS

Book 2
Word Bank Tests
Multiple Choice Tests
Partial Words Tests

How to use this pack to make the most of 11+ exam preparation

It is important to remember that for 11+ exams there is no national syllabus, no pass mark and no retake option! It is therefore vitally important that your child is fully primed in order to perform to the best of their ability to give themselves the best possible chance on the day.

Cloze Tests

Cloze Tests consist of passages with missing words that require the child to recognise and select the correct answer from a set of several options presented. Both comprehension and vocabulary are tested.

Never has it been more useful to learn from mistakes!

Students can improve by as much as 15% , not only by focused practice but also by targeting any weak areas.

How to manage your child's own practice

To get the most up-to-date information, log on to the Eleven Plus Exams website (www.elevenplusexams.co.uk). Eleven Plus Exams is the largest UK on-line resource with over 65,000 webpages and a forum administered by a select group of experienced moderators.

About the authors

The Eleven Plus Exams **First Past the Post®** series has been created by a team of experienced tutors and authors from leading British universities including Oxford and Cambridge.

Published by University of Buckingham Press
With special thanks to the children who tested our material at the ElevenPlusExams' centre in Harrow.
ISBN: 9781908684356

About Us

Eleven Plus Exams is the largest website in the UK that specifically prepares children for the 11 plus exams. The website offers a vast amount of information and advice on the 11 plus as well as a moderated online forum, books, downloadable material and online services to enhance your child's chances of success.

The company also provides specialist 11 plus tuition and is a supplier of online services to schools. Eleven Plus Exams is recognised as a trusted and authoritative source. It has been quoted in numerous national newspapers, including The Telegraph, The Observer, The Daily Mail and The Sunday Telegraph, as well as BBC Radio and national television (BBC1 and Channel 4).

Set up in 2004, the website grew from an initial 20 webpages to more than 65,000 today, and has been visited by millions of parents. The website gives impartial advice on exam preparation and techniques. It is moderated by over experts who provide support for parents both before and after the exams.

Visit our website and see why we are the market's leading one-stop shop for all your 11 plus needs.

- ✓ Comprehensive quality content and advice written by 11 plus experts
- ✓ Eleven Plus Exams online shop supplying a wide range of practice books, e-papers, software and apps
- ✓ Lots of FREE practice papers to download
- ✓ Professional tuition service
- ✓ Short revision courses
- ✓ Year-long 11 plus courses
- ✓ Mock exams tailored to reflect those of the main examining bodies

Other titles in the First Past The Post® Series

11+ Essentials Range of Books
VERBAL REASONING

ISBN	TITLE
9781908684288	Verbal Reasoning: Cloze Tests Book 1
9781908684356	Verbal Reasoning: Cloze Tests Book 2
9781908684639	Verbal Reasoning: Vocabulary Book 1 - Multiple Choice
9781908684783	Verbal Reasoning: Vocabulary Book 2 - Multiple Choice
9781908684844	Verbal Reasoning: Vocabulary Book 3 - Multiple Choice
9781908684646	Verbal Reasoning: Grammar and Spelling Book 1 - Multiple Choice
9781908684790	Verbal Reasoning: Grammar and Spelling Book 2 - Multiple Choice
9781908684868	Verbal Reasoning: Vocabulary in Context Level 1
9781908684875	Verbal Reasoning: Vocabulary in Context Level 2
9781908684882	Verbal Reasoning: Vocabulary in Context Level 3
9781908684889	Verbal Reasoning: Vocabulary in Context Level 4

ENGLISH

ISBN	TITLE
9781908684295	English: Comprehensions Book 1 Classic Literature
9781908684486	English: Comprehensions Book 2 Contemporary Literature
9781908684851	English: Comprehensions Book 3 Non-Fiction

NUMERICAL REASONING

ISBN	TITLE
9781908684431	Numerical Reasoning: Quick-Fire Book 1
9781908684448	Numerical Reasoning: Quick-Fire Book 2
9781908684653	Numerical Reasoning: Quick-Fire Book 1 - Multiple Choice
9781908684752	Numerical Reasoning: Quick-Fire Book 2 - Multiple Choice
9781908684301	Numerical Reasoning: Multi-Part Book 1
9781908684363	Numerical Reasoning: Multi-Part Book 2
9781908684769	Numerical Reasoning: Multi-Part Book 1 - Multiple Choice
9781908684776	Numerical Reasoning: Multi-Part Book 2 - Multiple Choice

MATHEMATICS

ISBN	TITLE
9781908684462	Maths: Mental Arithmetic Book 1
9781908684806	Maths: Worded Problems Book 1
9781908684936	Maths: Worded Problems Book 2
9781908684493	Maths Dictionary Plus

NON-VERBAL REASONING

ISBN	TITLE
9781908684318	3D Non-Verbal Reasoning Book 1
9781908684479	3D Non-Verbal Reasoning Book 2

PUZZLES

ISBN	TITLE
9781908684905	Puzzles: Maths Crosswords
9781908684912	Puzzles: Vocabulary

Test Paper Packs

ISBN	TITLE
9781908684103	English Practice Papers - Multiple Choice Pack 1
9781908684127	Verbal Reasoning Practice Papers - Multiple Choice Pack 1
9781908684134	Non-Verbal Reasoning Practice Papers - Multiple Choice Pack 1
9781908684110	Mathematics Practice Papers - Multiple Choice Pack 1

Contents

Contents

Section Three: Partial Words

Section Four: Mark Scheme

Once each test has been completed and marked using the answers at the back, you can use our 11+ Peer Compare System[TM] to anonymously compare your child's performance to peers who have completed the same test(s). Register at http://peercompare.elevenplusexams.co.uk and activate the access code printed on the front inside cover of this book.

Instructions

There are three Cloze passage question types included in this book that are designed to prepare your child for the new styles of 11 plus exams. We recommend these tests be used as real exam practice to benchmark your child's performance and gauge your child's reading, comprehension and vocabulary levels.

Word Bank Cloze Tests

These comprise passages in which several words are omitted and placed in a 'word bank' or list. The objective is to insert the correct words from the list into the appropriate blank spaces. This type of question relies on the child's understanding of the passage content to ascertain the accurate answer.

Multiple Choice Cloze Tests

Multiple Choice Cloze Tests consist of passages with missing words that require the child to recognise a correct answer from a set of three possible options. As well as testing vocabulary, these exercises also test how efficiently words are used in their correct context.

Partial Words Cloze Tests

Partial Words Cloze Tests include words in which several characters are missing, requiring the child to add the deliberately omitted letters from each word. The content of the passages provide clues to the incomplete words and tests the child's vocabulary.

BLANK PAGE

FIRST PAST THE POST®

Word Bank

Marking Grid						
Test	**1**	**2**	**3**	**4**	**5**	**6**
Score	/22	/23	/18	/16	/20	/25

Read the following instructions carefully:

1. In the following questions fill in the letters to complete the words in the passage, entering one letter per box.

2. The timer indicates how much time you have for the following passages.

3. Work as quickly and carefully as you can.

4. When you have finished a page, go straight onto the next page until you finish the test.

5. Write your answers clearly and legibly. You will get no marks for illegible answers.

6. To change your answer, rub out your old answer completely and then mark your new answer clearly.

7. If you cannot answer a question, go on to the next question.

8. When you reach the end go back and check all your answers for the remaining time.

Once you have completed each test and marked it using the answers at the back you can anonymously go online and compare your child's performance relative to peers who have completed the same test(s) using our 11+ Peer Compare System™. Register at http://peercompare.elevenplusexams.co.uk/ and then activate the access code supplied inside the front cover.

5 minutes

Word Bank					
contain	absorbing	surface	currents	moderating	functions
heating	summer	occupies	deepest		

Oceans

Around 70 percent of the Earth's **(1)**_____ is covered by oceans that

(2)_____ approximately 97 percent of the Earth's water supply. The largest and

(3)_____ of the oceans is the Pacific Ocean, which **(4)**_____ around a third

of the Earth's surface. Amongst their many **(5)**_____, oceans are responsible for

(6)_____ the Earth's temperature by **(7)**_____ heat energy from the Sun.

The ocean **(8)**_____ then distribute this energy around the planet, **(9)**_____

the land and air during the winter months, and cooling it down during the **(10)**_____.

Word Bank					
drowning	feet	sound	echo	awake	pod
comprising	emit	detect	currently	object	social

Dolphins

There are **(11)**_____ around 40 species of dolphin ranging in size from four to 30

(12)_____, and typically weighing from 100 to 22,000 pounds. They are very

(13)_____ animals and travel in pods **(14)**_____ between two and 15

dolphins, although **(15)**_____ sizes can vary depending on the activity undertaken.

Dolphins are unable to breathe underwater, so to prevent **(16)**_____ whilst asleep, half of

a dolphin's brain sleeps while the other half remains **(17)**_____, allowing it to continually

breathe. Dolphins navigate using a natural sonar called echolocation, whereby they

(18)_____ high frequency clicks through the water. Upon hitting an object, the

(19)_____ waves bounce off it and return, allowing the dolphin to **(20)**_____

the shape, size and speed of any **(21)**_____ solely from listening to the

(22)_____.

Test 2

Word Bank					
marshy	disease	infected	recovery	critical	tropical
derived	blood	diagnosis	breathing	insect	parasites

Malaria

Malaria is a **(1)**_____ disease caused by the bite of an **(2)**_____ female

mosquito. When such a mosquito bites you, it injects harmful **(3)**_____ into your body,

causing symptoms that typically include fever and headache. In **(4)**_____ cases, this can

lead to a coma or even death. Mosquitoes feed on **(5)**_____ and malaria is transmitted

from person to person every time the **(6)**_____ has a meal, thus making it contagious.

However, early **(7)**_____ and prompt treatment of the **(8)**_____ frequently

results in the victim making a full **(9)**_____. The name of the disease is

(10)_____ from two medieval Italian words 'mala' and 'aria', meaning 'bad air'. It was

once believed that malaria was caused by **(11)**_____ the bad air of

(12)_____ places.

4

Word Bank

salvage	naval	artefacts	armed	fleet	serving
maritime	seabed	display	battleship	Tudor	

The Mary Rose

Constructed between 1509 and 1511, the Mary Rose was King Henry VIII's favourite

(13)_____ and was named after his sister, Mary Tudor. As part of King Henry's vast

(14)_____ force, the Mary Rose was a new breed of ship, (15)_____ with a

powerful cannon and heavy guns.

However in 1545, following 33 years (16)_____ in several wars, the Mary Rose sank while

leading 60 ships against an attack by the French (17)_____. Despite Henry's attempts to

(18)_____ the magnificent ship, it remained on the (19)_____ until 1982,

when it was raised in what is considered one of the most complex undertakings in

(20)_____archaeology.

Along with the thousands of (21)_____ that were discovered on the ship, the Mary Rose

was placed on (22)_____ at the Historic Dockyard in Portsmouth, allowing us to learn and

enhance our knowledge about the (23)_____ period.

Word Bank					
Victorian	empire	powerful	existed	monarch	rule
India	reigning				

Queen Victoria

Queen Victoria was the head of an extensive **(1)**_____, and at 63 years and seven months,

served as the longest **(2)**_____ British monarch in history. Born in 1819, Victoria became

Queen in 1837 at the young age of 18 and was the first **(3)**_____ to reside at Buckingham

Palace. From 1876, she also served as the Empress of **(4)**_____ and spoke Hindi, German

and French in addition to English.

The period of Victoria's **(5)**_____ was marked by significant industrial, political, cultural

and scientific change and is thus known as the **(6)**_____ age. It was during this time that

Britain became one of the most **(7)**_____ countries in the world, with an empire larger

than had ever previously **(8)**_____.

Test 3 (continued)

Word Bank					
auditory	significance	activity	sacred	dreams	primarily
invoking	impaired	images	messages		

Dreams

Every person has **(9)**_____ and during a full eight hour sleep, two hours of it is spent

dreaming. Visually **(10)**_____ people who lost their sight after birth can see

(11)_____ in their dreams, whereas those who were born blind have

(12)_____ dreams that involve their sense of sound, as well as touch and smell. Dreams

(13)_____ occur in what is known as the rapid-eye movement (REM) phase of sleep, when

brain **(14)**_____ is considered high.

Over time, dreams have held varying **(15)**_____ for different cultures. For example, the

Greeks believed dreams were **(16)**_____ sent from ancient Gods, and would sometimes be

found sleeping in **(17)**_____ places in the hope that they would be conducive for

(18)_____ significant dreams.

Word Bank					
beloved	elevated	architecture	iconic	complete	focus
ultimate	dome	craftsmen	intricate	resting	marble
mausoleum	emperor	symmetrical	elegant		

Taj Mahal

Built entirely of white **(1)**_____, the Taj Mahal is a famous **(2)**_____ in India

and is considered one of the country's most **(3)**_____ landmarks and admired works of art.

It was built by the Mughal **(4)**_____ Shah Jahan, in memory of his third wife, Queen

Mumtaz Mahal, and it is her final **(5)**_____ place.

Many people describe the monument as the **(6)**_____ symbol of the emperor's love for his

(7)_____ wife to whom he had been married for 17 years. She died in 1631, which left the

emperor grief-stricken.

The construction of the **(8)**_____ building began in 1632 and took 20,000

(9)_____ nearly 22 years to **(10)**_____, at a cost of 32 million rupees. The

central **(11)**_____ of the monument is the tomb; an ornate white marble structure that

stands **(12)**_____ on a square plinth and comprises a **(13)**_____ building topped by a large white marble dome. The bulbous **(14)**_____ is one of the principal points

of the structure and rises to a height of 213 feet, and 58 feet in diameter. As impressive as the

(15)_____ of the Taj Mahal is, so too is the detail that has gone into embellishing the

exterior with **(16)**_____ calligraphy, sophisticated carvings and semi-precious stones.

Word Bank					
survival	accomplished	foundation	peak	shield	community
accountable	hierarchical	colonies	vitamins	forage	produce
insect	disease	fundamental	worker	consumed	generation
existed	organised				

The Honey Bee

The honey bee has **(1)**_____ for millions of years and is the only **(2)**_____ to

produce food that is **(3)**_____ by humans. The honey produced by bees not only contains

(4)_____, enzymes and minerals, but it is also a source of antioxidants that help to fight

(5)_____.

Honey bees live in **(6)**_____ communities called **(7)**_____ that can contain

up to 60,000 bees at any given time. To ensure the **(8)**_____ of a colony, bees abide by a

(9)_____ system that guarantees all the work is **(10)**_____, with each bee

fulfilling a specific role that serves the entire **(11)**_____. This includes nurse bees that look

after the young, worker bees, which **(12)**_____ for pollen and nectar and are

(13)_____ for feeding and bathing the queen, construction workers that build the

(14)_____ for the queen to lay eggs on, and guard bees that **(15)**_____

11

and protect her.

Although the **(16)**_____ bees tend to the queen bee's every need, this does not mean she

is without a **(17)**_____ task of her own. The queen bee is the only one in the colony to lay

eggs that will **(18)**_____ the hive's next **(19)**_____ of bees. With a life span

of up to five years, she spends each day laying eggs and at the **(20)**_____ of the breeding

season in the summer, she can lay as many as 2,500 eggs in a single day.

Word Bank					
malfunctioned	manual	flight	erosion	engineer	space
certificate	footprints	astronaut	dignitaries	lunar	aborted
impressionable	mankind	return	mesmerised	moon	immortalised
forced	phenomenal	crew	fuel	volcanic	surface
zeal					

Neil Armstrong

Born in 1930, Neil Armstrong was an American **(1)**_____ who is recognised for being the

first man to walk on the **(2)**_____. Prior to becoming a world-renowned astronaut,

Armstrong had a diverse career as an aerospace **(3)**_____, a test pilot, and a naval aviator.

He was also an officer in the U.S. Navy and served in the Korean War.

Armstrong developed a **(4)**_____ for flying and planes from a young age when his father

took him and his brother to the Cleveland Air Races. This comprised a series of **(5)**_____

air races that displayed the speed and reliability of aircraft and engines.

In 1936, at the **(6)**_____ age of five, Armstrong experienced his first flight in an airplane

and became **(7)**_____ by the experience. Several years later, he undertook flying lessons,

and by the age of 15, he had earned his flight **(8)**_____ even before he held a driver's license.

In 1962, he was selected by NASA to become an astronaut although Armstrong's first space

(9)_____ narrowly avoided disaster when one of the rocket's thrusters

(10)_____ and the spacecraft spun out of control. Although the spacecraft was brought

under control, the crew were **(11)**_____ to end the mission and return to Earth

prematurely as they had consumed most of the **(12)**_____.

Four years later, Armstrong was selected to be a member of the Apollo 11 mission that was to become

the first attempt at a manned **(13)**_____ landing. After several months of preparation and

practice, the crew of Apollo 11 left Cape Canaveral on 16 July 1969, watched by more than 3,000

journalists, 7,000 **(14)**_____, and approximately half a million tourists. A precarious and

unforeseen moment occurred during the flight where Armstrong had to take over

(15)_____ control of the lunar landing.

The pressure on him was immense, for if the landing took too long, the **(16)**_____ would

be left short on fuel and the mission would have had to be **(17)**_____. Fortunately, the

landing was successful and on 21st July 1969, Armstrong stepped on to the moon and uttered the now

(18)_____ words, "That's one step for man, one giant leap for (19)_____."

Along with Buzz Aldrin, Apollo 11's astronaut and pilot, Armstrong spent several hours exploring the lunar

(20)_____,where they collected rock samples and set up scientific experiments.

Decades later, the (21)_____ made by Armstrong and Buzz Aldrin remain on the surface,

for unlike Earth, there is no (22)_____ by wind or water on the moon because it has no

atmosphere.

Furthermore, with no (23)_____ activity to alter the features of the lunar surface, nothing

is washed away.

Upon their (24)_____ to Earth, the crew members were hailed as heroes and their

accomplishment served to place the United States at the forefront of the (25)_____

exploration race.

Multiple Choice

Marking Grid						
Test	7	8	9	10	11	12
Score	/20	/23	/22	/26	/17	/44

Read the following instructions carefully:

1. In the following questions fill in the letters to complete the words in the passage, entering one letter per box.

2. The timer indicates how much time you have for the following passages.

3. Work as quickly and carefully as you can.

4. When you have finished a page, go straight onto the next page until you finish the test.

5. Write your answers clearly and legibly. You will get no marks for illegible answers.

6. To change your answer, rub out your old answer completely and then mark your new answer clearly.

7. If you cannot answer a question, go on to the next question.

8. When you reach the end go back and check all your answers for the remaining time.

Once you have completed each test and marked it using the answers at the back you can anonymously go online and compare your child's performance relative to peers who have completed the same test(s) using our 11+ Peer Compare System™. Register at http://peercompare.elevenplusexams.co.uk/ and then activate the access code supplied inside the front cover.

Test 7

The Sahara Desert

The Sahara Desert is the world's hottest desert and is one of the harshest **[1]** ☐ environments / ☐ planets / ☐ cities on the

planet. It is also the third largest **[2]** ☐ desert / ☐ forest / ☐ tundra after the Arctic and Antarctica, and at over 9.4 million

square kilometres, it is almost as **[3]** ☐ vast / ☐ humble / ☐ diminutive as the United States or China. The Sahara Desert has a

[4] ☐ consistent / ☐ diverse / ☐ moderate climate ranging from more than 50 degrees Celsius in the **[5]** ☐ hottest / ☐ greatest / ☐ rainiest months, to

below zero during the **[6]** ☐ winter / ☐ spring / ☐ summer months. Given these extremes, it is **[7]** ☐ surprising / ☐ unsurprising / ☐ perplexing that it also

has one of the lowest population **[8]** ☐ varieties / ☐ densities / ☐ species , with only 2.5 million people **[9]** ☐ residing / ☐ resting / ☐ reclining in an

area of 3.5 million square miles.

Thousands of years ago, the Sahara had an **[10]** ☐ insufficient / ☐ minimal / ☐ abundant water supply to enable **[11]** ☐ extinction / ☐ survival / ☐ travel on the edge of the desert, but today, with the exception of a few **12** [ ] oases [ ] trees , and the Nile Valley, there is [ ] plants

13 [ ] destroy

little water to [ ] sustain   life in most parts of the desert.

[ ] deplete

The Amazon Rainforest

14 [ ] tropically

The Amazon Rainforest is a lush, [ ] tropical   natural resource covering 2.5 million square miles, or

[ ] meticulous

two thirds of South America, and is the largest rainforest in the world. Teeming with a **15** [ ] multitude [ ] hive   of [ ] colony

exotic plants, birds and animals, it is home to around 2.5 million different insect **16** [ ] speciality [ ] specialities , more [ ] species

17 [ ] society

than 40,000 plant species as well as [ ] indigenous tribes.

[ ] irrelevant

During the past 40 years, more than 20 percent of the Amazon Rainforest has disappeared because of

18

[ ] deforestation

[ ] defamation   where trees are cut down to make space for farming.

[ ] foraging

Test 7 (continued)

19

Consequently, this has resulted in the ☐ germination
☐ extinction of many plants and animals, despite a recent
☐ expulsion

20

☐ expansion
☐ resignation in deforestation rates.
☐ reduction

Test 8

6 minutes

Ancient Egypt

1 ☐ civilisations **2** ☐ archaeologists

Ancient Egypt is one of the most mysterious of all ☐ cities   and its numerous ☐ archaically
☐ municipals   ☐ archaeological

3 ☐ captivity

discoveries have become a perpetual source of ☐ captivation for archaeologists, academics, and
☐ contempt

historians.

4 ☐ evidence

Dating back to 3200 BC there has been much ☐ evidential that suggests Egypt was a rich, varied and
☐ rambling

5
☐ prosaic
☐ phosphorous civilisation. The ancient Egyptians were very **6** ☐ pariah
☐ prosperous   ☐ spiritual   and held a strong belief
☐ spirituality

7 ☐ forsaken

that when someone died their spirit remained permanently ☐ disengaged to their body; in order to
☐ connected

8 ☐ morals   **9** ☐ persevere
achieve ☐ immortality in the afterlife, it was deemed necessary to ☐ preserve   the body.
☐ morality   ☐ serve

10 ☐ mummery

Thus, they developed the process of ☐ mummification – a method of preserving bodies so they would
☐ mulching

11 ☐ distinguishable

remain lifelike ☐ perishable   and .
☐ unrecognisable

Test 8 (continued)

12
- [ ] idea
Mummification was an established [ ] belief primarily reserved for the wealthy and
- [ ] ritual

13
- [ ] powerful
- [ ] powerless ,
- [ ] meek

14
- [ ] exuberant
as poor people could not afford [ ] exorbitant the process.
- [ ] excavated

Native Americans

15
- [ ] habitats
The first [ ] inhabitants of North America were known as Native Americans and although they had
- [ ] cosmonauts

16
- [ ] preoccupied
- [ ] occupied   the land for thousands of years before the arrival of Europeans in the 15th century, it
- [ ] culminated

17
- [ ] citizens
was not until 1924 that they were all officially considered US [ ] tribes   .
- [ ] leaders

18
- [ ] pessimistic
They comprised hundreds of [ ] egocentric tribes. Depending on which tribe they belonged to and
- [ ] nomadic

19
- [ ] geographical
their [ ] preferred   location, Native Americans would either hunt, fish or
- [ ] geological

20
- [ ] cultivate
- [ ] captivate large crops
- [ ] capitulate

for food.

Test 8 (continued)

21

All Native Americans were very spiritual and ☐ adhered to many religious customs and beliefs. They
- ☐ adhesive
- ☐ order

22

worshipped many Gods but the ☐ surmount importance of food and crops meant they held the Sun
- ☐ paramount
- ☐ catamount

23

as a supreme God whom they recognised as a life-giving ☐ farce .
- ☐ force
- ☐ planet

John F Kennedy

John Fitzgerald Kennedy was born in Massachusetts on 29th May 1917 and became the 35th

1

☐ president
☐ emperor   of the United States of America. He was considered immensely popular and
☐ baroness

2

☐ charisma   **3**
☐ charismatic . Kennedy was ☐ cultivated
☐ magnetic   ☐ educated   at Harvard University and shortly after graduating joined
                    ☐ deduced

4

                    ☐ served
the US Navy where he ☐ commanded in the Second World War.
                    ☐ dominated

5

                              ☐ academia
At the age of 29 he entered the world of ☐ philanthropy and became a Democratic Congressman.
                              ☐ politics

6   **7**

☐ defeated   ☐ rejected
In 1960, Kennedy ☐ commended   Richard Nixon and became the youngest ☐ defected president
☐ congratulated   ☐ elected

of the United States. However, after serving only two years and ten months in office, on 2nd November

8   **9**

☐ ousted   ☐ oldest
1963 Kennedy was ☐ overthrown . He was 46 years of old and not only was he the ☐ youngest
☐ assassinated   ☐ quietest

president to be elected, but was also the youngest to die.

Test 9 (continued)

10
According to ☐ investigators / ☐ reformists / ☐ professor , a gunman called Lee Harvey Oswald killed him but many believe that

11
the president's death was the result of a ☐ ailment / ☐ conspiracy / ☐ truce . Nonetheless, this has never been

12
☐ proven / ☐ challenged . / ☐ believed

Tiger Snakes

13
There are a ☐ plasma / ☐ plethora / ☐ plank of snake species in the world many of which are

14
☐ auspicious / ☐ harmless / ☐ timely .

15
However, there are also ☐ pernicious / ☐ spacious / ☐ viscous venom-secreting snakes whose bites inflict poisonous wounds

which can be fatal if left untreated.

16
One of the world's most ☐ vicarious / ☐ vicious / ☐ placid snakes is reputed to be the Tiger Snake and is commonly found

17
in the ☐ temperature / ☐ temperate / ☐ Arctic climate of Southern Australia. The Tiger Snake gets its

18
☐ fearsome / ☐ cumbersome / ☐ irksome

reputation from the defensive position it takes when it is confronted or

19
- [ ] endangered
- [ ] protected
- [ ] unscathed

. Under the

threat of attack, the Tiger Snake will

20
- [ ] endow
- [ ] encircle
- [ ] endeavour

to frighten and intimidate its

21
- [ ] adversary
- [ ] adventurer
- [ ] anniversary

by

flattening its head and neck and

22
- [ ] elevating
- [ ] withdrawing
- [ ] lowering

its head high like a cobra.

Test 10

The Titanic

1

☐ luxury

The Titanic was a ☐ mediocre British ocean liner that left Southampton, England on her

☐ pitiable

2

☐ superstate

☐ maiden   voyage to New York City in 1912. Weighing more than 46,000 tons and reaching nearly

☐ flawless

3

☐ weight

900 feet in ☐ diameter , she was the world's largest passenger

☐ length

4

☐ yacht

☐ liner   of that time, whose

☐ catamaran

5

☐ inferior

luxurious and ☐ hideous accommodation was unrivalled by any other liner.

☐ lavish

6

☐ adorned

In addition to the opulent accommodation ☐ forlorn   with expensive furniture and decorations, the

☐ suborned

7

☐ attributed

Titanic also ☐ featured   a Turkish bath, fine restaurants, libraries, a swimming pool and an on-board

☐ nurtured

8

☐ pilots

gymnasium. Moreover, the ☐ crew   intended the ship to be more akin to a luxury

☐ designers

9

☐ floating

☐ stationary

☐ prevailing

hotel than a passenger liner.

10
□ fastest
The ship was also purported to be the □ safest   ship ever built, so much so that she only carried 20
□ weakest

11
□ lifeboats
□ lifejackets – enough to accommodate only half of the 2,200 passengers and crew
□ rings

12
□ abroad
□ aboard   in
□ abound

13
□ rationale
the event of a disaster. The □ ridicule   behind this was based on the
□ ratio

14
□ vehemently
□ narrowly   held belief
□ tenuously

15
□ sinkable
that the ship's construction made her □ unsinkable and lifeboats would only be necessary to rescue
□ stoppable

16
□ crews
□ survivors of other sinking ships.
□ animals

17
□ Fortunately
□ Tragically   , four days in to her first
□ Acoustically

18
□ carriage
□ voyage   , the Titanic struck an iceberg, causing five of
□ pilgrimage

19
□ compartments
her watertight □ windows   to flood. The ship gradually filled with the icy
□ stalls

20
□ carnivorous
□ tempestuous
□ petulant

21
□ copious
waters of the North Atlantic Ocean and sank to the bottom of it. The □ sufficient number of lifeboats
□ scant

22
□ ensured
aboard the ship □ ensued   that many passengers failed to find salvation and
□ endured

23
□ provocation
□ protection   ,
□ perdition

Test 10 (continued)

24
☐ rescuing
resulting in the ☐ drowning of 1,522 passengers and crew members. The sinking of the Titanic was
☐ immersing

25
☐ submersed   **26** ☐ life
one of the deadliest ☐ maritime   disasters in ☐ history .
☐ airborne   ☐ literature

Test 11

Alfred Bernhard Nobel

1
☐ designator
Alfred Nobel was a Swedish engineer, chemist and the ☐ inventor   of dynamite, who also established
☐ sculptor

2
☐ Nobel
the   ☐ Noble   Prize.
☐ Noodle

The son of an engineer and inventor, Alfred was born in 1833 and at the age of nine moved to Russia

3
☐ engineering
where his father had an ☐ enginery   company that provided
4
☐ defence
☐ defiance   weapons for the
☐ farming
☐ indifferent

Russian government.

5
☐ abroad
During his late teens, Alfred's father sent him ☐ abreast to study chemical engineering and during that
☐ aboard

6
☐ fortune
two-year period, he was ☐ hapless   to visit several countries including Germany, France and
☐ opportune

7
☐ departure
America. Upon his ☐ return   to Sweden, Alfred developed an
8
☐ apathetic
☐ acute   interest in the study
☐ retreat
☐ passing

of explosives, specifically in the safe manufacture and use of nitro-glycerine, a very

9
- [ ] volatile
- [ ] demure liquid
- [ ] sedate

explosive. He was all too

10
- [ ] unfamiliar
- [ ] familiar
- [ ] unacquainted

with the dangerous nature of the

11
- [ ] substance
- [ ] metal
- [ ] copper

as his

younger brother, along with several other people, were killed when a

12
- [ ] gas
- [ ] dynamite
- [ ] nuclear

explosion occurred

in Alfred's factory.

Before his death in 1896, Alfred

13
- [ ] wreathed
- [ ] inherited
- [ ] bequeathed

most of his vast fortune to

14
- [ ] establish
- [ ] establishment
- [ ] disinherit

annual prizes in Physics, Chemistry, Physiology or Medicine, Economics, Literature and Peace. These

became known as the

15
- [ ] redundant
- [ ] provident
- [ ] prestigious

Nobel Prizes and are awarded to organisations and individuals in

16
- [ ] acclimation
- [ ] acclamation
- [ ] acclivity

and recognition of scientific or cultural advances that have the greatest

17
- [ ] benefit
- [ ] detriment
- [ ] impediment

to humanity.

Test 12

Mother Teresa

1
☐ missionary
Mother Teresa was a Catholic nun and ☐ mercenary , devoted to caring for the sick and poor. She was
☐ merchant

2
☐ devilishly
born Agnes Bojaxhiu in the Republic of Macedonia in 1910 to ☐ devoutly Catholic parents of Albanian
☐ flexibly

3
☐ decent
☐ descent   .
☐ decadence

4
☐ unwarranted   **5** ☐ quelled
From a young age, an ☐ moderate   commitment to charity was ☐ distilled in Mother Teresa, a
☐ intense   ☐ instilled

6
☐ repugnant
commitment that was to become ☐ prevalent throughout her life. By the time she reached the age of
☐ ominous

7
☐ ultimate
12, Agnes felt God's calling and was convinced that her ☐ frivolous purpose in life was to spread the
☐ equivocal

8
☐ Christianity
word of ☐ profanity   .
☐ inhumanity

9
☐ preserve
However, it was not until 1928 that she decided to ☐ admonish her worldly possessions and become a
☐ relinquish

Test 12 (continued)

nun. Agnes left home and headed to Dublin, Ireland, to join a **10** [ ] colony / [ ] community / [ ] conglomerate   of Catholic nuns with

missions in India and it was while she was there that she **11** [ ] bestowed / [ ] resumed / [ ] assumed   the name Sister Mary Teresa. A

few months later, Mother Teresa travelled to India where she took her **12** [ ] scared / [ ] sacred / [ ] scold   vows as a nun and

commenced teaching in a **13** [ ] convent / [ ] convalescent / [ ] confounding   school in Calcutta.

During this time, she became **14** [ ] affluent / [ ] fluent / [ ] effluent   in speaking Hindi and Bengali and through education,

15 [ ] lethargically / [ ] dubiously / [ ] ardently   devoted herself to **16** [ ] alleviating / [ ] exacerbating / [ ] accumulating   poverty. However, the **17** [ ] impious / [ ] pious / [ ] impervious   nun

was deeply affected by the suffering and poverty she **18** [ ] witnessed / [ ] corroborated / [ ] yielded   beyond the convent walls, and

she sought **19** [ ] permission / [ ] condemnation / [ ] emaciation   from her superiors to leave her teaching post and **20** [ ] transfuse / [ ] peruse / [ ] pursue   a

newfound calling to work amongst the sick and **21** [ ] embellished / [ ] impoverished / [ ] unvanquished   poor in the slums of Calcutta.

Test 12 (continued)

22
- notoriously
- sequentially
- subsequently

She ☐ established an open air

23
- school
- jail
- pool

☐ for slum children and a home for the dying

24
- prescriptive
- deciduous
- decrepit

and disadvantaged in a ☐ building, successfully persuading the city

25
- authorities
- civilisation
- Christianity

☐ to

26
- appreciative
- initiative
- selective

donate to her charitable ☐ .

27
- adulation
- congregation
- corporation

It was not long before Mother Teresa's ☐ named, 'the Missionaries of Charity' expanded

28
- consideration
- avocation
- donations

with new members. At around the same time, financial ☐ from across the world poured

29
- exponential
- implausible
- excavated

in, enabling the ☐ expansion of Mother Teresa's charity; the primary

30
- subjective
- operative
- objective

☐ of

31
- rejected
- indulged
- interjected

which was to care and love people who had been ☐ and abandoned by society. Over a ten

32
- colony
- company
- cacophony

year period, her charity set up a leper ☐ , an orphanage, a nursing home, centres for the

33
- able
- disabled
- capable

blind and ☐ , assistance for victims of floods,

34
- mimics
- hypodermics
- epidemics

☐ , and famine, as well as a

32

35
series of vital mobile health [ ] clinics [ ] communes . In 1965, Mother Teresa focussed her efforts on [ ] cities

36
[ ] national
[ ] international expansion, opening up houses and
[ ] shrinking

37
[ ] traditions
[ ] affirmations in dozens of countries in Europe,
[ ] foundations

Asia, Africa and America.

38
Her relentless efforts and [ ] fervent [ ] indifferent commitment to help the sick and [ ] apathetic

39
[ ] fortuitous
[ ] fortunate   earned
[ ] unfortunate

40
Mother Teresa countless [ ] escapades [ ] accolades   , including the Nobel Peace Prize in recognition of her [ ] disparagement

41
[ ] inhumane
[ ] humanitarian work. By the time of Mother Teresa's death in 1997, the Missionaries of Charity had
[ ] human

42
[ ] succeeded
[ ] conceded   in establishing 610 foundations in 123 countries across all seven
[ ] forfeited

43
[ ] cosmonauts
[ ] continents   .
[ ] consonants

44
Due to her unwavering dedication and [ ] treachery [ ] inconsistency in helping those in need, Mother Teresa will [ ] steadfastness

be remembered as one of the greatest humanitarians of the 20th century.

BLANK PAGE

Partial Words

Marking Grid						
Test	13	14	15	16	17	18
Score	/23	/19	/20	/13	/18	/30

Read the following instructions carefully:

1. In the following questions fill in the letters to complete the words in the passage, entering one letter per box.

2. The timer indicates how much time you have for the following passages.

3. Work as quickly and carefully as you can.

4. When you have finished a page, go straight onto the next page until you finish the test.

5. Write your answers clearly and legibly. You will get no marks for illegible answers.

6. To change your answer, rub out your old answer completely and then mark your new answer clearly.

7. If you cannot answer a question, go on to the next question.

8. When you reach the end go back and check all your answers for the remaining time.

Once you have completed each test and marked it using the answers at the back you can anonymously go online and compare your child's performance relative to peers who have completed the same test(s) using our 11+ Peer Compare System™. Register at http://peercompare.elevenplusexams.co.uk/ and then activate the access code supplied inside the front cover.

6 minutes

Body Language

Body language refers to the **(1)** pr☐ces☐ of communicating non-verbally through

our **(2)** g☐stur☐s, postures, movement and facial **(3)** ☐xp☐e☐s☐o☐s.

According to many experts, it **(4)** ☐mp☐ise☐ between 50 and 70 percent of all

human communication. Your entire **(5)** ☐o☐y, from your eyes down to your feet

(6) co☐vey☐ an expression that directly **(7)** c☐rrel☐t☐s to your emotional

state. For example, when you feel confident you will **(8)** s☐bc☐nscio☐s☐y

project strong positive body language and stand tall with your head **(9)** ☐e☐d high.

Brain research suggests that whatever you are feeling first **(10)** man☐fest☐ itself in

your body and only later does it register in your **(11)** c☐n☐ciou☐ mind. In the

same **(12)** ve☐n, when you adopt **(13)** af☐irm☐tiv☐ body language you begin

to feel more **(14)** c☐☐fide☐☐ as there is a close connection between your

psychology and **(15)** ph☐siol☐g☐.

Iceland

Iceland is an island situated near the Arctic Circle and is the most **(16)** spa☐sel☐

populated country in Europe. The country lies on two tectonic **(17)** p☐at☐s, along

which more than 150 volcanoes are located, although not all of them are

(18) ☐ct☐v☐. Other spectacular **(19)** phen☐men☐ include towering glaciers,

mineral-rich mud pools, **(20)** g☐yser☐, and thundering waterfalls. Most of the

country's power comes from **(21)** rene☐ab☐e sources with approximately 30

percent of its electricity generated from **(22)** g☐oth☐rma☐ energy, and the rest

generated by **(23)** hyd☐op☐wer. This makes Iceland one of the world's most

environmentally friendly places.

Charles Dickens

Born in 1812, Charles Dickens was an **(1)** es☐eem☐d Victorian author of classic

literary novels; including 'Great Expectations' and 'Oliver Twist', which are still

(2) ext☐nsi☐ely read today. When Charles was 12 years old, his father was

(3) imp☐is☐ned for debt and Charles was forced to leave school to work at a

rodent-ridden factory for **(4)** me☐s☐y wages. Here, he was exposed to the

(5) gri☐ reality of his **(6)** s☐t☐atio☐ where child labour was commonplace and

adults seldom displayed **(7)** c☐mp☐ssio☐ towards children. Three years later,

Charles returned to school but is **(8)** ble☐k experience of the world had left an

(9) ind☐libl☐ impression on him, and one that he frequently

(10) i☐lustr☐te☐ in his novels. He died of a stroke in 1870 and is

(11) ☐u☐i☐d at Westminster Abbey.

Albert Einstein

Albert Einstein was born in 1879 and is considered to be the most

(12) ☐rom☐n☐nt and influential physicist of the 20th century, but he is best

known for developing the theory of relativity. **(13)** He fe☐ven☐ly challenged widely

accepted notions about the nature of physics.

While the subject **(14)** perp☐ex☐d many eminent scientists, from an early age

Einstein appeared to have a clear view of the complexities of physics and demonstrated

an **(15)** un☐av☐ring determination and steadfastness to solve them. As well as

being a **(16)** r☐now☐e☐ scientist, Einstein was also a **(17)** p☐cifis☐ and

humanitarian, urging nations to live in peace. In 1921, he won the Nobel Prize for

Physics and because of his great **(18)** int☐ll☐ctu☐l achievements, Einstein's

name has become **(19)** sy☐onym☐u☐ with genius.

The Blue Whale

The blue whale is the largest animal known to have ever **(1)** ☐x☐ste☐ and can

grow to a **(2)** s☐bst☐nti☐l length of 100 feet and can exceed 150 tons in weight,

making them **(3)** ext☐ns☐v☐ly larger than a dinosaur! In fact, these mammals

are so **(4)** ma☐si☐e that their blood vessels are wide enough for humans to swim

through and their tongues alone can weigh as much as an elephant. In comparison to

its **(5)** mo☐umen☐al size, it is surprising that this ocean giant consumes

(6) h☐mong☐us quantities of **(7)** dim☐nut☐v☐ shrimplike creatures called

krill each day.

The Tower of London

The Tower of London is a historic **(8)** c☐st☐e situated on the north bank of the

River Thames, whose **(9)** ☐is☐o☐y dates back almost 1,000 years. It was founded

by William the Conqueror in 1066, following his successful **(10)** i☐va☐io☐ of

England and is one of the world's few surviving intact **(11)** m☐di☐val buildings.

Although it is best known as a **(12)** n☐tori☐us prison, the Tower of London has also

served as a Royal Palace, a **(13)** f☐rtr☐ss, a Royal Zoo, a public records office, a

home for the Royal Mint and the Crown Jewels, which have been on

(14) ☐i☐pl☐y there since the late 17th century. Every evening, a

(15) t☐adi☐i☐nal ceremony takes place to lock up and **(16)** ☐ecu☐e the

Tower of London. Despite the fact that the **(17)** ☐onar☐h does not reside at the

Royal Palace, the 700 year old **(18)** ☐itu☐l of securing the fortress each night is still

(19) imp☐rat☐ve as aside from the Crown Jewels, it also houses other valuable

(20) a☐tef☐cts.

Michelangelo Buonarotti

Michelangelo Buonarotti was born in 1475 and is considered to be one of the most

(1) d☐st☐ngui☐he☐ artists of the Italian **(2)** Rena☐ss☐nc☐. He

considered himself a sculptor but is most renowned for painting the vast ceiling of the

(3) illus☐ri☐us Sistine Chapel in Rome.

Built in the 1470s, the Sistine Chapel is the best known in Vatican City, and each year

five million people flock to it to marvel at Michelangelo's **(4)** metic☐lou☐

masterpiece. The chapel's paintings took four years to complete, and cover an

(5) e☐pan☐iv☐ area of 12,000 square feet, which is about one-sixth of the size of

a football pitch. The paintings **(6)** dep☐c☐ Biblical stories about the creation,

downfall and **(7)** red☐mptio☐ of mankind. More than 300 figures were painted on

the ceiling, all of them unique in **(8)** ass☐rte☐ poses.

Although Michelangelo was mostly known as an **(9)** em☐nen☐ sculptor and

painter, he was also a **(10)** pro☐ifi☐ poet and composed more than 300 pieces of

poetry during his life time.

While his paintings are greatly **(11)** a☐m☐red by millions of people, Michelangelo

himself was a **(12)** reti☐en☐ and sometimes melancholic individual, who believed

that **(13)** s☐li☐ude was essential to creating works of art.

Test 17

Mount Kilimanjaro

At 5,895 metres above sea level with its snow capped peak and **(1)** g☐ac☐er☐,

Mount Kilimanjaro is the tallest mountain in **(2)** ☐f☐☐ca and the world's highest

freestanding **(3)** m☐☐n☐ai☐. Its majestic **(4)** h☐ig☐t has led to it

being dubbed, 'The Roof of Africa'.

Kilimanjaro is the fourth highest of the Seven **(5)** ☐um☐i☐s - the highest peaks

on each of the seven **(6)** co☐t☐n☐nt☐ and is situated 205 miles south of the

(7) ☐qu☐t☐r on Tanzania's border with Kenya. It is composed of three

(8) d☐sti☐ct volcano peaks: Kibo, Mawenzi and Shira. Although two peaks are

extinct, Kibo remains **(9)** ☐orm☐nt and could potentially erupt. The last significant

(10) e☐upt☐on is estimated to have been 360,000 years ago.

The plant life and **(11)** s☐e☐er☐ on Kilimanjaro is very diverse, ranging from

(12) rai☐f☐r☐s☐, moorland, alpine desert, to sub-zero **(13)** z☐ne☐ as you

get nearer to the summit. Each zone, **(14)** ☐niq☐e in its features and climate,

is home to different plants and life forms.

The higher up the mountain you climb, the **(15)** ☐h☐n☐er the air becomes and

once you reach a high **(16)** a☐t☐t☐d☐ there is only half the oxygen available

than there is at sea level, thus becoming **(17)** i☐c☐ea☐in☐l☐ difficult to

(18) ☐re☐t☐e.

The Great Fire of London

The Great Fire of London is one of the most well known **(1)** disa☐ter☐ in London's

history. It started with just one spark in the **(2)** ☐ous☐ of a baker on Pudding Lane

on 2ⁿᵈ September 1666 and came to an end on 5ᵗʰ September, lasting four days.

During this period, most of the shops and houses in London were built from wood and

as the streets of London were very **(3)** n☐rro☐, the houses were built close

together. Furthermore, the area surrounding Pudding Lane was home to

(4) s☐vera☐ warehouses that stored rope, timber and oil. This meant they were

highly **(5)** fl☐mm☐bl☐, and the fire quickly spread between the closely built

buildings. This was compounded by the fact that it was a windy morning, which caused

the hot **(6)** ☐mbers to be blown from roof top to roof top.

The **(7)** r☐gin☐ blaze spread to the east, west and north of London. Fortunately,

the buildings on the south of the River **(8)** Tha☐e☐ were spared from the damage

because the fire was unable to spread across London Bridge.

As the fire continued on its path of **(9)** des☐ruct☐on, the smoke could be seen

from afar as Oxford, such was the **(10)** s☐veri☐y. Many frightened people gathered

as many of their **(11)** bel☐ngi☐gs as they could carry and tried to board boats to

flee to safety. Others found safety in fields outside of London where they took

(12) shel☐e☐ in shacks and tents. In a bid to stop the fire, Londoners tried to fight

it with buckets of water but the **(13)** m☐gnit☐de of the fire ensured their

efforts were ineffective.

Test 18 (continued)

Other attempts to control the **(14)** bl☐z☐ included using long fire hooks to pull

down any houses that sat in the direct path of the fire to create fire-breaks, hence

(15) depr☐vin☐ the fire of fuel. These efforts also proved to be futile because pull-

ing down the houses this way was very time **(16)** con☐um☐ng, and in the

meantime the wind blew the fire across the fire-breaks.

On the third day of the fire, Tuesday 4th September, **(17)** g☐npow☐er was used to

blow up houses and buildings in another bid to prevent the fire from spreading

further. This effort, combined with the wind dropping and changing direction, allowed

the people of the city to gain **(18)** con☐r☐l of the blaze. The fire was eventually

(19) exti☐g☐ishe☐ and all that remained was the aftermath of the

(20) ☐nfer☐o.

The damage caused by the fire was extensive and a third of London was destroyed with

some places **(21)** sm☐ulde☐ing for months. 373 acres of the city had been

burned, Newgate and Ludgate prisons were reduced to ashes and St Paul's Cathedral

was **(22)** rui☐e☐. Even its lead roof had been **(23)** m☐lte☐. In total, more than

13,000 houses, 84 **(24)** chu☐che☐ and 44 halls were burned down. In addition,

100,000 people were made **(25)** h☐mel☐ss and the cost of the damage was exten-

sive. It took 50 years to **(26)** rebu☐l☐ the burned area of the city.

Following the Great Fire, new **(27)** regul☐ti☐ns were put in place to prevent it

ever happening again. Narrow streets became a thing of the past and all houses were

required to be made with **(28)** bri☐☐ or stone instead of wood. Thatch roofs were

also **(29)** f☐rb☐dden and had to be substituted with slate or tile. The

(30) Gre☐☐ Fire of 1666 changed London forever.

BLANK PAGE

FIRST PAST THE POST®

Answers

Once you have completed each test and marked it using the answers at the back you can anonymously go online and compare your child's performance relative to peers who have completed the same test(s) using our 11+ Peer Compare System™.

Register at http://peercompare.elevenplusexams.co.uk/ and then activate the access code printed on the front inside cover.

Your unique 16 digit access code is inside the front cover

Word Bank Answers

TEST 1	
Page 2	
Oceans	
(1)	surface
(2)	contain
(3)	deepest
(4)	occupies
(5)	functions
(6)	moderating
(7)	absorbing
(8)	currents
(9)	heating
(10)	summer
Dolphins	
(11)	currently
(12)	feet
(13)	social
(14)	comprising
(15)	pod
(16)	drowning
(17)	awake
(18)	emit
(19)	sound
(20)	detect
(21)	object
(22)	echo

TEST 2	
Page 4	
Malaria	
(1)	tropical
(2)	infected
(3)	parasites
(4)	critical
(5)	blood
(6)	insect
(7)	diagnosis
(8)	disease
(9)	recovery
(10)	derived
(11)	breathing
(12)	marshy
The Mary Rose	
(13)	battleship
(14)	naval
(15)	armed
(16)	serving
(17)	fleet
(18)	salvage
(19)	seabed
(20)	maritime
(21)	artefacts
(22)	display
(23)	Tudor

TEST 3	
Page 6	
Queen Victoria	
(1)	empire
(2)	reigning
(3)	monarch
(4)	India
(5)	rule
(6)	Victorian
(7)	powerful
(8)	existed
Dreams	
(9)	dreams
(10)	impaired
(11)	images
(12)	auditory
(13)	primarily
(14)	activity
(15)	significance
(16)	messages
(17)	sacred
(18)	invoking

Word Bank Answers

	TEST 4
	Page 8
	Taj Mahal
(1)	marble
(2)	mausoleum
(3)	iconic
(4)	emperor
(5)	resting
(6)	ultimate
(7)	beloved
(8)	elegant
(9)	craftsmen
(10)	complete
(11)	focus
(12)	elevated
(13)	symmetrical
(14)	dome
(15)	architecture
(16)	intricate

	TEST 5
	Page 10
	The Honey Bee
(1)	existed
(2)	insect
(3)	consumed
(4)	vitamins
(5)	disease
(6)	organised
(7)	colonies
(8)	survival
(9)	hierarchical
(10)	accomplished
(11)	community
(12)	forage
(13)	accountable
(14)	foundation
(15)	shield
(16)	worker
(17)	fundamental
(18)	produce
(19)	generation
(20)	peak

	TEST 6
	Page 12
	Neil Armstrong
(1)	astronaut
(2)	moon
(3)	engineer
(4)	zeal
(5)	phenomenal
(6)	impressionable
(7)	mesmerised
(8)	certificate
(9)	flight
(10)	malfunctioned
(11)	forced
(12)	fuel
(13)	lunar
(14)	dignitaries
(15)	manual
(16)	crew
(17)	aborted
(18)	immortalised
(19)	mankind
(20)	surface
(21)	footprints
(22)	erosion
(23)	volcanic
(24)	return
(25)	space

Multiple Choice Answers

TEST 7		TEST 8		TEST 9	
Page 16		**Page 19**		**Page 22**	
The Sahara Desert		**Ancient Egypt**		**John F Kennedy**	
(1)	environments	(1)	civilisations	(1)	president
(2)	desert	(2)	archaeological	(2)	charismatic
(3)	vast	(3)	captivation	(3)	educated
(4)	diverse	(4)	evidence	(4)	served
(5)	hottest	(5)	prosperous	(5)	politics
(6)	winter	(6)	spiritual	(6)	defeated
(7)	unsurprising	(7)	connected	(7)	elected
(8)	densities	(8)	immortality	(8)	assassinated
(9)	residing	(9)	preserve	(9)	youngest
(10)	abundant	(10)	mummification	(10)	investigators
(11)	survival	(11)	distinguishable	(11)	conspiracy
(12)	oases	(12)	ritual	(12)	proven
(13)	sustain	(13)	powerful	**Tiger Snakes**	
The Amazon Rainforest		(14)	exorbitant	(13)	plethora
(14)	tropical	**Native Americans**		(14)	harmless
(15)	multitude	(15)	inhabitants	(15)	pernicious
(16)	species	(16)	occupied	(16)	vicious
(17)	indigenous	(17)	citizens	(17)	temperate
(18)	deforestation	(18)	nomadic	(18)	fearsome
(19)	extinction	(19)	geographical	(19)	endangered
(20)	reduction	(20)	cultivate	(20)	endeavour
		(21)	adhered	(21)	adversary
		(22)	paramount	(22)	elevating
		(23)	force		

Multiple Choice Answers

	TEST 10
	Page 25
	The Titanic
(1)	luxury
(2)	maiden
(3)	length
(4)	liner
(5)	lavish
(6)	adorned
(7)	featured
(8)	designers
(9)	floating
(10)	safest
(11)	lifeboats
(12)	aboard
(13)	rationale
(14)	vehemently
(15)	unsinkable
(16)	survivors
(17)	Tragically
(18)	voyage
(19)	compartments
(20)	tempestuous
(21)	scant
(22)	ensured
(23)	protection
(24)	drowning
(25)	maritime
(26)	history

	TEST 11
	Page 28
	Alfred Bernhard Nobel
(1)	inventor
(2)	Nobel
(3)	engineering
(4)	defence
(5)	abroad
(6)	opportune
(7)	return
(8)	acute
(9)	volatile
(10)	familiar
(11)	substance
(12)	dynamite
(13)	bequeathed
(14)	establish
(15)	prestigious
(16)	acclamation
(17)	benefit

	TEST 12
	Page 30
	Mother Teresa
(1)	missionary
(2)	devoutly
(3)	descent
(4)	intense
(5)	instilled
(6)	prevalent
(7)	ultimate
(8)	Christianity
(9)	relinquish
(10)	community
(11)	assumed
(12)	sacred
(13)	convent
(14)	fluent
(15)	ardently
(16)	alleviating
(17)	pious
(18)	witnessed
(19)	permission
(20)	pursue
(21)	impoverished
(22)	subsequently
(23)	school
(24)	decrepit
(25)	authorities
(26)	initiative
(27)	congregation
(28)	donations

Multiple Choice Answers

TEST 12 (continued)	
(29)	exponential
(30)	objective
(31)	rejected
(32)	colony
(33)	disabled
(34)	epidemics
(35)	clinics
(36)	international
(37)	foundations
(38)	fervent
(39)	unfortunate
(40)	accolades
(41)	humanitarian
(42)	succeeded
(43)	continents
(44)	steadfastness

Partial Words Answers

TEST 13

Page 36

Body Language

(1)	process
(2)	gestures
(3)	expressions
(4)	comprises
(5)	body
(6)	conveys
(7)	correlates
(8)	subconsciously
(9)	held
(10)	manifests
(11)	conscious
(12)	vein
(13)	affirmative
(14)	confident
(15)	physiology

Iceland

(16)	sparsely
(17)	plates
(18)	active
(19)	phenomena
(20)	geysers
(21)	renewable
(22)	geothermal
(23)	hydropower

TEST 14

Page 37

Charles Dickens

(1)	esteemed
(2)	extensively
(3)	imprisoned
(4)	measly
(5)	grim
(6)	situation
(7)	compassion
(8)	bleak
(9)	indelible
(10)	illustrated
(11)	buried

Albert Einstein

(12)	prominent
(13)	fervently
(14)	perplexed
(15)	unwavering
(16)	renowned
(17)	pacifist
(18)	intellectual
(19)	synonymous

TEST 15

Page 38

The Blue Whale

(1)	existed
(2)	substantial
(3)	extensively
(4)	massive
(5)	monumental
(6)	humongous
(7)	diminutive

The Tower of London

(8)	castle
(9)	history
(10)	invasion
(11)	medieval
(12)	notorious
(13)	fortress
(14)	display
(15)	traditional
(16)	secure
(17)	Monarch
(18)	ritual
(19)	imperative
(20)	artefacts

Partial Words Answers

TEST 16

Page 39

Michelangelo Buonarotti

(1)	distinguished
(2)	Renaissance
(3)	illustrious
(4)	meticulous
(5)	expansive
(6)	depict
(7)	redemption
(8)	assorted
(9)	eminent
(10)	prolific
(11)	admired
(12)	reticent
(13)	solitude

TEST 17

Page 40

Mount Kilimanjaro

(1)	glaciers
(2)	Africa
(3)	mountain
(4)	height
(5)	Summits
(6)	continents
(7)	equator
(8)	distinct
(9)	dormant
(10)	eruption
(11)	scenery
(12)	rainforest
(13)	zones
(14)	unique
(15)	thinner
(16)	altitude
(17)	increasingly
(18)	breathe

TEST 18

Page 41

The Great Fire of London

(1)	disasters
(2)	house
(3)	narrow
(4)	several
(5)	flammable
(6)	embers
(7)	raging
(8)	Thames
(9)	destruction
(10)	severity
(11)	belongings
(12)	shelter
(13)	magnitude
(14)	blaze
(15)	depriving
(16)	consuming
(17)	gunpowder
(18)	control
(19)	extinguished
(20)	inferno
(21)	smouldering
(22)	ruined
(23)	melted
(24)	churches
(25)	homeless
(26)	rebuild
(27)	regulations
(28)	brick
(29)	forbidden
(30)	Great